Idioms Workbook

HarperCollins*Publishers*

second edition 2002

HarperCollins Publishers
Westerhill Road, Bishopbriggs, Glasgow G64 2QT,
Great Britain

www.cobuild.collins.co.uk

ISBN 0-00-713400-2

Corpus Acknowledgements

We would like to acknowledge the assistance of the many hundreds of individuals and companies who have kindly given permission for copyright material to be used in the Bank of English. The written sources include many national and regional newspapers in Britain and overseas; magazine and periodical publishers; and book publishers in Britain, the United States and Australia. Extensive spoken data have been provided by radio and television broadcasting companies; research workers at many universities and other institutions; and numerous individual contributors. We are grateful to them all.

Author Acknowledgement

We would like to thank the author of the first edition of the COBUILD Idioms Workbook, Malcolm Goodale, for his work in creating the original text, on which we have based this edition.

Note

Typeset by Rosetta Publishing, Peebles

Printed and bound in Great Britain by Montgomery Litho Group

Contents

Introduction

The **Collins COBUILD Idioms Workbook** can be used on its own or in conjunction with the new second edition of the **Collins COBUILD Dictionary of Idioms**. This new second edition of the workbook practises 100 of the most important idioms in both British and American English. The examples and exercises have been thoroughly updated for this new edition, using information from the *Bank of English*.

Why use idioms?

Idioms exist in all languages. They form an important part of everyone's vocabulary and are used in both formal and informal language, but are much more common in informal, spoken English. They should not, however, be confused with slang, which is very often inappropriate in certain social situations.

We use idioms:

- to be amusing or witty
- to play with words
- to be different
- to put other people at ease, even in the most formal situations
- to express something which other words do not quite express
- to communicate more clearly and more visually

Understanding idioms

Many idioms are easy to understand. Look at the idiom *'to sweep something under the carpet'*, for example. If you understand the words 'sweep', 'under' and 'carpet', there's a very good chance that you'll understand the figurative meaning of the idiom. Other idioms, such as *'at loggerheads'* or *'in the doldrums'* may be more difficult to understand because of their low frequency vocabulary.

Many English idioms can be translated into other languages almost word for word; many others can be easily understood because the meaning is translatable, but not the words. Other idioms can be impossible to translate: these are often idioms which express cultural concepts.

Origins of idioms

A word of warning. Phrases become idioms when they are not used with their original literal meaning. Native speakers will often play with the double meanings, literal and figurative, to make an amusing comment. Consider this example:

Eurotunnel, understandably, is much happier than the ferry companies, given projections which suggest it will leave them high and dry.

If someone *leaves you high and dry*, they leave you in a difficult situation and you are unable to do anything about it.

This idiom originally applied to ships, which were literally left high and dry when the tide went out. The writer of the above example knows the origin of the idiom and probably used it here deliberately to talk about ferry companies. Some common origins which form the basis of idioms are: the sea and navy; the army; domestic life; farming and animals; sports and games; and parts of the body.

Understanding the origin of an idiom can help you to understand how it is used figuratively. You can find out more about the origins of idioms in the new second edition of the **Collins COBUILD Dictionary of Idioms**.

Idioms Workbook

There are 15 units in this workbook. The Introductory Unit introduces some of the most common difficulties with idioms. The following 14 Units organize idioms by theme, for example starting and stopping, money, honesty and fairness etc. Contrasting idioms are presented in the same Unit. This allows you to build up a greater understanding of the exact meaning of each idiom.

The idioms practised in Units 1–14 are common to all parts of the English-speaking world. Regional variations are noted in the Language Comment sections in each unit. For example, *the icing on the cake* , which is used in British English, is practised in Unit 2, with its American form, *the frosting on the cake* noted in the Language Comment section in the same unit.

Unit exercises

There are between five and eleven idioms in each Unit. Each Unit starts with a list of the idioms you will be studying, followed by an example sentence using each idiom. All of the examples are real English, taken from our vast database of written and spoken English, the *Bank of English*. The exercises also contain real examples from the *Bank of English*, so you can be sure that you are studying English idioms as they are really used. The Language Comment section highlights any similar or related idioms, explains difficult vocabulary, and draws your attention to any grammatical or usage restrictions.

The first exercise in each Unit asks you to complete the definitions of the idioms in the Unit. In this way, you can build up a record of these important idioms and their meanings. The next exercises involve choosing the idiom that best fits in the sentence. The final exercise in each Unit asks you to write a paragraph on one of three given topics, including some of the idioms you have studied in the unit. Many learners are able to understand idioms in reading, but find it difficult to use them properly in their own written and spoken English. These exercises will help you to practise this by using the idioms in context. It is a good idea, if possible, to check the paragraphs with a teacher or a native speaker of English.

Answer key

This section provides the answers to all the exercises in the workbook.

We hope that you will enjoy using this workbook. We always welcome feedback from learners and teachers, so if you have any comments, you can contact us on our website at:
http://www.cobuild.collins.co.uk
by email directly to: cobuild@ref.collins.co.uk
or you can write to us at the following address:

Collins COBUILD
Westerhill Road
Bishopbriggs
Glasgow G64 2QT
UK

A Meanings and idioms

The idioms in this book are organized into Units according to meaning. To familiarize yourself with this system, match the following categories of meaning with the idioms.

A Disagreement *B Honesty and fairness* *C Decisions*

D Starting and stopping *E Deception, hiding, and revealing*

1 **sit on the fence** ________

'We're going to sit on the fence and wait until next week before making a decision,' said trainer Luca Cumani.

2 **set the ball rolling** ________

On February 25th he set the ball rolling when he presented to EU ministers a new report on the consequences of reform by NERA, an economic consultancy.

3 **sweep something under the carpet** ________

People often assume if you sweep something under the carpet the problem will go away, but that is not the case.

4 **not see eye to eye with someone** ________

The Prime Minister did not see eye to eye with him on this issue.

5 **stab someone in the back** ________

She seemed to be incredibly disloyal. She would be your friend to your face, and then stab you in the back.

B Grammar and idioms

The most common grammatical patterns in idioms are the following:

1 Verb + noun

e.g. **bite the bullet** (Unit 9)

2 Adjective + noun

e.g. **red tape** (Unit 9)

3 Prepositional idioms

e.g. **at loggerheads** (Unit 10)

4 Combinations of the above

e.g. **put something on the back burner** (Unit 2)

Put each of the following idioms in the correct place in the table according to their grammatical pattern.

in the doldrums **rock the boat** **the pecking order**

a vicious circle **turn a blind eye to sth** **from scratch**

turn over a new leaf **break the ice**

verb + noun	
adjective + noun	
prepositional idiom	
combination of types	

C Variations in idioms

Many idioms are fixed and the words which make them up cannot be changed. Sometimes, however, you have a choice of words. For example:

He decided to throw/chuck/toss in the towel/sponge.

There are several possible combinations with this idiom. For example, you can use the verbs 'throw', 'chuck' or 'toss', and you can use the nouns 'towel' or 'sponge'. This information is often given in the Language Comment sections or shown in the exercises and examples. You should use a good dictionary to help you with difficult idioms. Possible ways in which idioms can vary are:

A verb change

e.g. **throw** in the towel → **chuck** in the towel

B noun change

e.g. throw in the **towel** → throw in the **sponge**

C preposition change

e.g. **under** par → **below** par

D used as an adjective

e.g. break the ice → **ice-breaking**

E used as a noun

e.g. sit on the fence → **fence-sitting**

F word(s) removed

e.g. Every cloud has a silver lining → a silver lining

G word(s) added

e.g. toe the line → toe the **party** line

Match the following examples for the idiom* jump on the bandwagon *with the variations listed above. Some examples may have more than one of the variations mentioned. The first example has been done for you.

If you say that someone, especially a politician, has *jumped on the bandwagon*, you disapprove of their involvement in an activity or movement, because you think that they are not strictly interested in it but are involved in it because it is likely to succeed or it is fashionable.

Examples		**Answers**
1	*It seems that every few months there's a new nutritional bandwagon you can climb on.*	A, G
2	*They came on the bandwagon after three other important computer retail groups agreed to become Apple dealers.*	
3	*Bandwagon-jumping is not always bad.*	
4	*Thorn EMI and hotels group Forte joined the bandwagon.*	
5	*In saying that, Clinton is climbing aboard a bandwagon which already has considerable momentum in the US.*	
6	*I see that Jane Gordon has hurled herself upon that already overloaded bandwagon by criticizing the money paid to our members of Parliament.*	

Don't worry – not all idioms allow this much variation!

D Restrictions

Some idioms have grammatical restrictions. Others have usage restrictions, which means that they are most commonly used in a particular grammatical form. The three areas which may cause difficulty for learners are:

negative and positive   singular and plural   active and passive

1 Negative and positive

Most idioms can be used in both a positive and a negative way, but some are only or more commonly used in one of the two ways. For example, the idiom *make headway* is more commonly used in a positive way.

If you *make headway*, you make progress in the thing you are trying to achieve.

Look at the following examples for the idiom* make headway *and write down whether they are used in a positive or a negative way.

Examples		**Positive or negative**
1	*The psychiatrist didn't make much headway.*	____________
2	*The Democrats have made significant headway.*	____________
3	*He suggested in fact that they were making little headway.*	____________
4	*He said he is not disappointed at the failure to make headway towards resolving differences.*	____________
5	*It makes it easier for beginners at the game to make some headway.*	____________

2 Singular and plural

The idioms listed below do not allow any singular/plural change. This means that you cannot say: *out on limbs* or *the icing on the cakes*. Many idioms, however, can be used in both the singular and plural form, though they are often more common in one or the other.

Sort the following idioms into two groups and write down whether the underlined noun is in the singular or plural.

Idioms		**Singular or plural**
1	stick to your guns	____________
2	the icing on the cake	____________
3	at arm's length	____________
4	pull strings	____________
5	out on a limb	____________
6	get on someone's nerves	____________

3 Active and passive

Although many idioms cannot be used in the passive, many others are frequently used in this way. For example, the idiom *nip in the bud* can be used in both the active and the passive.

If you *nip something in the bud*, especially something bad, you stop it at an early stage before it can develop into something worse.

Look at these examples for the idiom* nip in the bud *and write down which ones are in the passive and which ones are not.

Examples		**Active or passive**
1	*That's another disgraceful thing which has to be nipped in the bud.*	____________
2	*There's no reason why that shouldn't have been nipped in the bud a long time ago.*	____________
3	*I managed to nip that in the bud.*	____________
4	*She thought she had nipped the problem in the bud but instead Stanley became increasingly rude at school.*	____________
5	*It has to be nipped in the bud.*	____________

hear something on the grapevine	**out of your depth**
off the record	**put your finger on something**
read between the lines	**bear something in mind**
get the hang of something	**cross your mind**
a rule of thumb	

Study the following examples to try and understand the underlined idioms in context.

hear something on the grapevine

It is so difficult to prove players have been induced to change clubs for money, yet you hear it on the grapevine and it gives the game a bad name.

off the record

'Let me tell you something off the record, Nigel, that we know unofficially that you have been followed for three days.'

read between the lines

You as a reader have to be vigilant in detecting biases – both those that are openly stated and those you have to read between the lines.

get the hang of something

It's a brilliant sport. You should expect to fall over a couple of times but you quickly get the hang of it.

a rule of thumb

...the general rule of thumb is the smaller the chilli, the hotter it is.

out of your depth

...if you ever feel out of your depth, just click on Help and we'll come to your rescue.

put your finger on something

'It's a dismal period and I suppose I can blame the Government though I can't put my finger on why exactly. I just feel they could do more.'

bear something in mind

'But I would ask you to remember that I also am involved in this expedition into the unknown.' 'I'll bear it in mind', Newman replied, and drank the rest of his coffee as the ship's engines slowed and the 'Georg Ots' prepared to dock in Soviet territory.

cross your mind

The thought instantly crossed my mind that she might be lying about her age.

Meaning

Using your understanding of the sentences above, complete the following definitions with the correct idioms.

1 If you ______________________________ an activity, you learn how to do it competently.

2 If you ______________________________, you hear about it from people you know.

3 If you are ______________________________, you feel anxious and inadequate because you have to deal with a situation or subject which you know very little about.

4 If something ______________________________, you suddenly think of it.

5 If you ____________________, you understand what somebody really means, or what is really happening in a situation, even though it is not stated openly.

6 If you ______________________________, for example a problem or an answer, you realize what it is and identify it.

7 A ____________________ is a general rule about something which you can be confident will be right in most cases.

8 If you say that your remarks are ____________________, you mean that you do not want anyone to report what you said.

9 If you tell someone to ______________________________, you are reminding or warning them about something important which they should remember.

Practice

A ***Select the correct idiom A, B or C to complete the following sentences.***

1 'Dr Barth, what is the greatest single thought that ever ____________________?'

A *read between the lines* *B* *crossed your mind* *C* *got the hang of it*

2 Perhaps this should be ____________________, but I don't think it really matters.

A *off the record* *B* *on the grapevine* *C* *out of your depth*

3 One frequently cited ____________________ for public works projects holds that every billion dollars invested in public works creates upwards of 40,000 jobs.

A *reading between the lines* *B* *off the record* *C* *rule of thumb*

4 'It's really terrific once you ____________________.' For the next ten minutes, he kept up a steady, one-sided conversation about the joys of windsurfing.

A *put your finger on it* *B* *get the hang of it* *C* *are out of your depth*

5 He had started writing novels before going to Nairobi and, having ____________________ that one of his efforts was to be published, he left his job and flew to Paris to join Anna.

A *put his finger on it* *B* *read between the lines* *C* *heard on the grapevine*

6 'I'd appreciate it if you'd be nice to him. He's young and a bit ______________.'

A *out of his depth* B *off the record* C *rule of thumb*

7 Even so, stress is an inescapable part of life. As stress expert Hans Selye has said, complete freedom from stress is death. It's worth ____________________, since we so often think of stress as an entirely bad thing.

A *hearing it on the grapevine* B *getting the hang of it* C *bearing this in mind*

8 'I haven't been playing as well as I know I can but I simply can't ______________ the reason.

A *read between the lines* B *get the hang of* C *put my finger on*

9 'I think that the great genius of Cole Porter was the fact that he could be extremely explicit, and you don't have to ________________________ too deeply to see exactly what he's really getting at.'

A *hear on the grapevine* B *get the hang of it* C *read between the lines*

B ***Complete the following sentences with one of the idioms in this unit, paying special attention to the verb forms.***

1 To listen well, you must concentrate, evaluate and understand whatever it is the other person's telling you. It means ______________________. A good listener really tries to understand what the other person is saying and then lets him or her know that he understands.

2 'We ________________________________ that he was leaving politics well before the announcement,' she said.

3 Complete, clear instructions for the use of the Permuterm indexes are in the front of each volume. If you have trouble ________________________ it, your reference librarian can help you.

4 It's ridiculous how such silly little things can sometimes take on a sudden importance in your life and you cannot ____ the reason. You laugh at them just as you always did, how absurd they are. And yet you go along with it all and feel you haven't the strength to stop.

5 'Total Recall' and 'Back to the Future III' all made something around $100 million, which sounds like a lot of money, except that they all cost about $60 million to produce. And the _________________________ in Hollywood is that you have to make $2^{1}/_{2}$ times your investment or you don't start to make a profit because so much is tied up in overheads.

6 Many of the current books on the subject will give you clear and detailed advice on how to deal with these questions, and most important of all, will give clear indications on when you may be getting ____ and should seek professional help.

7 US officials said Mr Taylor never gave the BBC an interview on the subject. They said his remarks were actually made ______________________________ and that someone had taped them and mailed the tape to BBC headquarters in London.

8 It may be worth approaching other recruitment organisations, but ______________________________ that they may charge a fee for their services.

9 Steve would rouse me from sleep at 2:00 a.m. with a phone call to chat about an idea that suddenly ______________________________.

Consolidation

Write a paragraph on one of the following topics, using at least four of the idioms you have studied in this unit.

1 Gossip.

2 Wonderful news.

3 The secret.

UNIT 2: IMPORTANCE AND PRIORITIES, DECISIONS

the tip of the iceberg	**sit on the fence**
the bottom line	**up in the air**
put something on the back burner	**stick to your guns**
the icing on the cake	

Study the following examples to try and understand the underlined idioms in context.

the tip of the iceberg

There are fears in Brussels that what has been revealed so far is only the tip of the iceberg and that organized crime and some bureaucrats are taking advantage of lax management controls to systematically rip off the EU.

the bottom line

'He likes issues to be brief and clear-cut. He then makes up his mind quickly. His strength is to assess what is happening and then go straight to the bottom line.'

put something on the back burner

Hopes were high as people looked forward to a new life free of shelter-linked disasters. But people's dreams have once again been put on the back burner[1] *as they concern themselves with survival from one day to the next.*

the icing on the cake

We were captivated, laughing and gasping as the screen sprang to life with text, sound, animation, even video. It seemed almost magical, and the fact that it was educational was the icing on the cake[2]*.*

sit on the fence

Now that people feel they have more money in their pockets I think people who have been sitting on the fence[3] *will now get off it and buy their homes.*

up in the air

I have heard that the position of coach is up in the air, but it would be unprofessional of me to inquire about it just as I am taking up a new appointment.

stick to your guns

Fashion retailer Alexon is sticking to its guns. Despite problems in the High Street and its own falling profits, it has not gone down the route of price discounting to bring customers through the door.

LANGUAGE COMMENT

[1] **Put something on ice** means the same as **put something on the back burner**.

[2] **The frosting on the cake**, which is American English, means the same as **the icing on the cake**.

[3] Verbs such as 'stay' and 'be' can also be used instead of 'sit' in this idiom.

Meaning

Using your understanding of the sentences above, complete the following definitions with the correct idioms.

1 If you describe something as ________________________, you mean that it is an extra good thing that happens and makes a situation or activity even better.

2 You say that someone is ________________________________ to express your disapproval of them for refusing to state a definite opinion about something or to say who they support in a conflict.

3 If you ________________________, you refuse to change your decision or opinion about something, even though other people are trying to tell you that you are wrong.

4 In a discussion or argument, if you describe one particular point as ____________________ ____________________, you mean that it is the most important and fundamental part of what you are discussing.

5 If you describe something as ___________________________, you mean that it is part of a very large problem or a very serious situation, although the rest may not be obvious or fully known about.

6 If an important decision or plan is ________________________, it has not been decided or settled yet.

7 If you put a project or issue __________________________, you decide not to do anything about it until a later date, because you do not consider it to be very urgent or important.

Practice

A ***Select the correct idiom A, B or C to complete the following sentences.***

1 They really believe in what I do and they want to enable me to do it,' and she went on to explain her success: 'I'm very good, that's ____________________.'

A the bottom line *B the tip of the iceberg* *C the back burner*

2 Then he became really ill and put all his plans______________________.

A on the tip of the iceberg *B on the fence* *C on the back burner*

3 'If she doesn't agree, nothing happens. So it's been left ___________, and there's no resolution.'

A up in the air *B on the fence* *C the icing on the cake*

4 The cost of fraud in the UK more than doubled between 1987 and 1991. The figures are based on cases where charges have been brought so this is just ____________________.

A the icing on the cake *B the bottom line* *C the tip of the iceberg*

5 'At this time in history, there's no time for subtlety or ______________. From now on, you're either with us or against us.'

A *sticking to your guns* *B* *sitting on the fence* *C* *putting it on the back burner*

6 'Our first-half display was brilliant, although City came back at us in the second half, but the last two goals were __________________________ for us.'

A *the tip of the iceberg* *B* *the icing on the cake* *C* *sitting on the fence*

7 We believe that if we __________________________, the people who are holding these hostages will understand that no way will we budge without our prisoners being included in the deal.

A *are up in the air* *B* *put it on the back burner* *C* *stick to our guns*

B ***Complete the following sentences with one of the idioms in this unit, paying special attention to the verb forms.***

1 I can't really say too much about who else I'm going to be working with at the moment because it's very much ____________________ and anything could happen.

2 Yet on the key issue of opting out, which is perhaps the most important to face parents since 1945, the commission has chosen, extraordinarily to __________________________, murmuring that schools must decide for themselves.

3 'Divorce is one of the most expensive activities in Britain', says Karen Matterson of the One Plus One marriage research centre, which produced the figures. But £1.4 billion is only ______________________________. Added to that you have the cost of absenteeism due to stress or attending court and also the cost to the NHS of stress-related illnesses that divorce can produce.

4 ______________________ is that vitamins are good for you, just exercise a little bit of common sense and don't go over the recommended daily dose.

5 Once you have decided what is and isn't acceptable, ________________________________ despite your child's protests – it's worth it in the end. When it begins to sink in that you mean what you say, he will stop making so many demands.

6 'Teaching has always been my main source of income, writing textbooks has only ever been ______________________________ and I don't expect that to change.'

7 Cultivate the friendships that enrich your life and get rid of the ones that do nothing for you or at least ____. There are also old friends who need you, whom you must not abandon.

Consolidation

Write a paragraph on one of the following topics, using at least three of the idioms you have studied in this unit.

1 A big decision.

2 A surprise.

3 The manager.

UNIT 3: COMMUNICATION, HELP AND ENCOURAGEMENT

on the same wavelength	**a silver lining**
hit it off	**a pat on the back**
break the ice	**in the same boat**

Study the following examples to try and understand the underlined idioms in context.

on the same wavelength

Not only did we understand each other, Steve and I rejoiced in our similar reactions to the world. We could complete each other's sentences because we were on the same wavelength.

hit it off

They hit it off, they made each other laugh, they had the same interests, they enjoyed each other's company. After a year of meeting socially and just being friends he finally asked her out on a real date, but she said no, saying that what she wanted was friendship and she didn't want to ruin that.

break the ice

We start the party with a bizarre game of bingo to break the ice and within minutes, everyone is making a complete idiot of themselves. Everyone has been given the name of an animal and when one of our numbers is called we have to make that animal's noise.

a silver lining

'Every cloud has a silver lining[1] in the medical world,' says author Andrew Nikiforuk. In his new book The Fourth Horseman, published by Fourth Estate, he points out that diseases led directly to the development of life-saving drugs.

a pat on the back

Mr Brooke deserves a pat on the back for tendering his resignation. He is one of the old school who still believes in honour in public life and his actions yesterday showed that. Too many members of the Cabinet, past and present, have shown a far more shallow view of their responsibilities.

in the same boat

'If we think our problems are unusual, we doubt we'll find solutions; once we know that other people have been in the same boat, we can help to teach each other. In my classes and workshops, I ask the participants to listen to other women's complaints about their mothers in new ways.'

LANGUAGE COMMENT

[1] **A silver lining** comes from the proverb **every cloud has a silver lining**.

Meaning

Using your understanding of the sentences above, complete the following definitions with the correct idioms.

1 If you say a bad or unpleasant situation has a ____________________, you mean that there is a good or pleasant side-effect of it.

2 If you say that someone should get __________________________ for doing something, you mean that they can expect to be rewarded or congratulated for it.

3 If two people _____________________ when they first meet, they find that they like each other or get on well together and have many things in common.

4 If you say that two people are _____________________, you mean that they understand each other well because they share the same attitudes, interests and opinions.

5 If you say that two or more people are ___________________________, you mean that they are in the same unpleasant or difficult situation.

6 If you _____________________ at a party or meeting, or in a new situation, you say or do something to make people feel relaxed and comfortable.

Practice

A ***Select the correct idiom A, B or C to complete the following sentences.***

1 Helen was able to comfort Nicholas's mother Susan, 40, when they met recently. 'We were two mothers ____________________ and able to make each other feel better.'

A *in the same boat* B *patting each other on the back* C *breaking the ice*

2 To ____________________ and discuss plans for the future service, I invited all three for drinks at my home in Temple Fortune.

A *break the ice* B *hit it off* C *be in the same boat*

3 'People my own age seem so immature. I just don't seem to be _____________________.'

A *a silver lining* B *in the same boat* C *on the same wavelength*

4 'When the chairman invited me round to his house I honestly thought it was to receive a wage increase, or at least ________________________. Instead, he said it's all over.'

A *a silver lining* B *a pat on the back* C *the same wavelength*

5 He's hideously over-educated; she's a good-hearted dunce. But they manage to __________________, despite the cultural gap.

A *hit it off* B *have a silver lining* C *be in the same boat*

6 She's still got a long way to go with her therapy, but at least now she can see ________________, not just a big black cloud.

A *the same boat* B *the same wavelength* C *the silver lining*

B ***Complete the following sentences with one of the idioms in this unit, paying special attention to the verb forms.***

1 If you don't understand something, don't be afraid to ask for clarification. Others will probably be ______________________ and be grateful for the chance to get it cleared up.

2 The Times finds space for an article that finds ________________________ in increased prices at the pumps. If petrol prices are kept high, might this not, the article muses, help in the fight against pollution?

3 Michael Aspel's wife Lizzie deserves ________________________. Anyone who puts her career on ice for ten years to look after her children has her heart in the right place.

4 'What I really love is his artistic personality. We are ____________________________, appreciate the same things. I feel I have found part of me.'

5 'Hodgson met Caroline, the new woman in his life, at a business dinner in January. They ________________ straight away,' a close friend of Hodgson's said yesterday. 'They both love outdoor pursuits, and Howard admires women with a good business brain.'

6 In Hollywood, Brecht was an obscure, non-English speaking writer with no money and no known background in the movies. And Brecht's demeanor did not help to ___________ _______________. He was, said John Houseman, absolutely open in his contempt for the movies as a medium for him to work in.

Consolidation

Write a paragraph on one of the following topics, using at least three of the idioms you have studied in this unit.

1 My best friend.

2 The party.

3 A problem shared is a problem halved.

UNIT 4: INVOLVEMENT AND INTEREST

steer clear	**give someone the cold shoulder**
at arm's length	**turn a blind eye to something**
keep something at bay	**have an axe to grind**
keep a low profile	**jump on the bandwagon**

Study the following examples to try and understand the underlined idioms in context.

steer clear

Age remains the most common prejudice. Gordon Methven suggests that older applicants should target smaller companies. 'They often welcome big company training and expertise, and maturity,' he says. He also advises them to steer clear of young managing directors who tend to recruit young teams.

at arm's length

The abiding danger for the media is that it becomes part of the political establishment it is meant to be covering. Broadcasters are often far too timid in their political reporting, newspaper journalists too cosy with those they are writing about. The media shouldn't always operate at arm's length from the political classes and sometimes, if it is doing its job properly, hostilities should break out.

keep something at bay

Bereavement and loneliness in all its forms is a universal phenomenon, and the problem is how to keep it at bay[1] so that it doesn't become overwhelming.

keep a low profile

They're so guilty about the amount of money they're earning they've decided to keep a low profile. They don't want to be noticed any more.

give someone the cold shoulder

Scientists say tobacco is as addictive as heroin. But the money tobacco companies give to minority and women's groups may be equally habit-forming. For years, when other companies were giving these groups the cold shoulder, the tobacco industry was there with generous contributions. But young women and minorities are also among those most affected by smoking and its related illnesses, leading critics to charge that what tobacco companies are really buying is silence.

turn a blind eye to something

Many customs officers turn a blind eye to limited amounts of goods being imported, preferring to concentrate their efforts on stopping drug and arms smuggling rather than on enforcing what is widely regarded as an iniquitous level of customs tax.

have an axe to grind

What makes Mr Sudetic's book compelling is that he has no axe to grind[2]. Unlike so many others, he tells the whole story, not the bits that support one side or the other.

jump on the bandwagon

We've got low unemployment, mortgages are cheap and cheap consumer credit. It's a good situation to buy in. We don't think house prices are being overvalued. Some people say you shouldn't jump on the bandwagon. But if you wait, you can expect to see prices go up by 9.5 per cent next year, so you'll end up paying more.

LANGUAGE COMMENT

[1] **Keep something at bay** is particularly common in written English.

[2] In American English, **axe** is usually spelt **ax**.

Meaning

Using your understanding of the sentences above, complete the following definitions with the correct idioms.

1 If you ______ something ________, you keep it from attacking you or affecting you in some other way. You can also ________ people ________.

2 If someone deliberately ignores you, you can say that they ____________ ____________.

3 If you say that someone is ______________, you are criticizing them for getting involved in something that is currently popular in order to get some advantage for themselves.

4 If you say that someone ______________, you mean that they have particular attitudes and prejudices about something, often because they think they have been treated badly or because they want to get a personal advantage.

5 If you keep someone ______________, you avoid being friendly with them or getting emotionally involved with them.

6 If you ______________ something, you deliberately ignore it because you do not want to take any action over it, even though you know you should.

7 If you ______________ of something or someone, you deliberately avoid them. If you ________ someone ________ of something, you help them to avoid it.

8 If someone ______________, they avoid doing things that will make people notice them.

Practice

A ***Select the correct idiom A, B or C to complete the following sentences.***

1 When the crowd heard that the children were in the school, it erupted into violent demonstrations, and with the police barely able to ______________, Huckaby had to arrange the hasty departure of her new pupils.

A give it the cold shoulder *B keep it at bay* *C jump on the bandwagon*

2 'I think people find it very hard to identify that there's a problem. Most people want their marriages to work and will ____________________ to some of the difficulties that may be getting in the way of making them work.'

A *have an axe to grind* B *turn a blind eye* C *keep a low profile*

3 'We present the facts as they are. We don't have any political bias, nor do we ____________________.'

A *steer clear* B *give the cold shoulder* C *have an axe to grind*

4 At the centre of this spreading reputation, Mackay Brown ____________________, delighted to be told that he looks more like a local fisherman than a poet.

A *keeps me at arm's length* B *gives me the cold shoulder* C *keeps a low profile*

5 The variety and quality on offer have improved tremendously over the last ten years. Even the large bakeries have tried to ____________________, producing baguettes, rye bread and the like, but their insistence on using inferior, cheaper flour means they fail to produce really good bread.

A *have an axe to grind* B *keep a low profile* C *jump on the bandwagon*

6 Her book is chilling in its description of what it feels like to ____________________ by Hollywood. The unreturned phone calls, the sudden cancellations of deals, the former friends who ignore you.

A *steer clear* B *be given the cold shoulder* C *have an axe to grind*

7 To avoid making the room too dark, ____________________ dark-coloured carpets.

A *turn a blind eye to* B *give the cold shoulder to* C *steer clear of*

8 The Guardian is unhappy about the trend towards honouring newspaper editors, and says many in the trade believe the press and politicians are best when they stay ____________.

A *on the bandwagon* B *kept at bay* C *at arm's length*

B *Complete the following sentences with one of the idioms from this unit, paying special attention to the verb forms.*

1 He didn't expect the high street banks to ______________________________ when he went to them with a business proposition. In the end, he sold his house, moved into rented accommodation and borrowed money from his mother.

2 A whole range of viruses are responsible for coughs, sore throats, runny noses and general weakness. Normally, the body's own defences can ______________ these ______________, but at Christmas we are particularly vulnerable because of too much rich food, too much partying and too little sleep.

3 The princess appealed to young people to ____________________ of the dangers of drugs.

4 Home, particularly when surrounded by his family, is where Eastwood is most comfortable. 'I've always been down to earth,' he explained. 'I never wanted to be famous, so I like to ____________________. My wife and I are invited to many functions in Dublin, Belfast and London but we rarely go.' He prefers to spend time with his grandchildren.

5 A person who has received their full share of reassuring physical contact from infancy will be able to weather the most adverse circumstances. You can also distinguish those people who have been brought up ______________________. Jeanette says: 'You can tell by the body movements – stiff walk, hunched shoulders, an awkward handshake – that they were not touched enough as children.'

6 I ______________________ either way on the subject of home-schooling, I don't even have children. However, most of Christopher Bantick's anti-home schooling article seemed to be just unsubstantiated statements of opinion and scare-mongering.

7 Unfortunately, many farmers are ______________________ and advertising organically grown food when in reality it takes up to ten years for all the harmful chemicals to disappear from the soil.

8 If someone else's baby is screaming as their hassled parent tries to pack their shopping, you don't actually have to do anything. But why not try being a 'good neighbour' instead of ______________________? Offer to lend a hand, either with packing the shopping or amusing the baby while they get the job done.

Consolidation

Write a paragraph on one of the following topics, using at least four of the idioms you have studied in this unit.

1 The political campaign.

2 An argument.

3 Friendship.

UNIT 5: STARTING AND STOPPING

from scratch	**nip something in the bud**
call it a day	**turn over a new leaf**
set the ball rolling	

Study the following examples to try and understand the underlined idioms in context.

from scratch

If eventually they are able to return home, they will have to start again from scratch. Oxfam is providing long term help for many refugee groups who are working to build new lives, either back home or in their new surroundings.

call it a day

My friend said he had only caught two small fish and was ready to call it a day, but as we had travelled 100 miles, I wanted another half hour.

set the ball rolling

A fierce price war is now underway with all the big supermarket rivals cutting prices, and casualties are inevitable. Sainsbury set the ball rolling last week with 30% discounts on a wide range of brands.

nip something in the bud

Even if your company doesn't have a workplace scheme, managers who spot problems early can do a great deal to help their employees, and themselves, by suggesting counselling. In this way, problems that can lead to depression and even illness can be nipped in the bud.

turn over a new leaf

I've turned over a new leaf because I've stopped drinking and tried to be a lot more professional in my approach to the game.

Meaning

Using your understanding of the sentences above, complete the following definitions with the correct idioms.

1 If someone has ______________________________, they have started to behave in a better or more acceptable way than previously.

2 If you ________ a bad situation or bad behaviour ______________________, you stop it at an early stage, before it can develop and become worse.

3 If you start ________________________, you create something completely new, rather than adding to something that already exists.

4 If you ______________________________, you start an activity or you do something which other people will join in with later.

5 If you ______________________________, you decide to stop doing something, usually because you are tired or are bored with it.

Practice

A ***Select the correct idiom A, B or C to complete the following sentences.***

1 'Who knows, maybe Paula and I will start a family in the near future.' While Emilio has ______________________________, his 31-year-old brother Charlie, star of the hit movie Platoon, can still be spotted in the bars along Sunset Strip.

A *started from scratch* B *been nipped in the bud* C *turned over a new leaf*

2 'I love chat shows and documentaries with a bit of human interest. It's no secret I want Alan Whicker's job when he ______________________. That's my great ambition. I never miss his programmes.'

A *nips in the bud* B *calls it a day* C *sets the ball rolling*

3 One experienced governor said last night that unless a riot was __________________ within the first few minutes, the only alternatives were a siege or the use of fire-power, and that would be unacceptable in Britain.

A *started from scratch* B *nipped in the bud* C *called it a day*

4 Put mildly, if we had to __________________ every day, we would not get a whole lot done.

A *start from scratch* B *turn over a new leaf* C *set the ball rolling*

5 My desk is threatening to collapse under the weight of the many tomes of writers' recollections that have appeared or are about to appear. Jon Stallworthy __________________, then there's been, let's see, Christopher Logue, Michael Holroyd, Al Alvarez and Edward Said.

A *called it a day* B *turned over a new leaf* C *set the ball rolling*

B ***Complete the following sentences with one of the idioms in this unit, paying special attention to the verb forms.***

1 'Well, I've got a lot more to say but I'm not going to say it because I don't want to go on for longer than I said I would so I think what we'll do now is ______________________. Thank you all for being so attentive and if anybody has any questions, I'll try and answer them.'

2 'I thought, well, I've been very privileged for the first fifteen years of my life but now I'm going to have to get on with it like Dad did. He started ________________________ and made his own way. Now I have to do the same.'

3 I was in prison a few years back but have since ______________________________.

4 In making his announcement, Duke said that he had ______________________________ on a number of key issues, including welfare and US immigration policy.

5 We have lived through a privileged period recently; we haven't come across many disastrous diseases and the ones that have presented themselves we have largely ______________________________.

Consolidation

Write a paragraph on one of the following topics, using at least two of the idioms you have studied in this unit.

1 New Year's Day.

2 The millionaire.

3 Resigning.

UNIT 6: QUALITY AND EFFORT

keep you on your toes	**pull your weight**
not up to scratch	**cut corners**
worth their salt	**a track record**

Study the following examples to try and understand the underlined idioms in context.

keep you on your toes

I hope you all heard what Pamela just said. She read ahead in the textbook. I'd like you to try to keep that in mind. On occasion, I might jump ahead a bit and spend a period covering a topic we've not yet studied at length. I do this from time to time to keep you on your toes. I'm very concerned about the amount of apathy I find in so many students today.

not up to scratch

Mr Moss said that if a candidate's skills were not up to scratch[1] *for a specific position, they could train at the facility for free until they reached the desired level.*

worth their salt

Any sailor worth his salt will tell you that a good fall of rain calms the surface of the sea.

pull your weight

You must remember that your performance will be judged by the performance of your team, and you cannot afford to carry members who are not pulling their weight.

cut corners

Although trees were crashing around the house, as the winds howled, she sat there totally unafraid. For she knew how she had built that house. She hadn't cut corners. She hadn't compromised her standards. She built it the right way.

a track record

The Home Office is looking for a person with experience of policing in London, a period spent in the provinces and a proven track record in energetic and innovative leadership.

LANGUAGE COMMENT

[1] **Under par**, **below par** and **not up to par** have similar meanings to **not up to scratch**. **Up to snuff** means almost the same as **up to scratch**, but is more common in American English.

Meaning

Using your understanding of the sentences above, complete the following definitions with the correct idioms.

1 If you say that no person ______________________ would do a particular thing, you are emphasizing that you would not respect or admire anyone who did that thing.

2 If someone ______________________, they work as hard as everyone else who is involved in the same task or activity.

3 If you say that someone or something is ______________________, you mean that they are not as good as they ought to be.

4 If you talk about the ______________________ of a person, company or product, you are referring to the reputation they have, which is based on all their successes and failures in the past.

5 If you ______________________, you save time, money or effort by not following the correct procedure or rules for doing something.

6 If you say that someone or something ______________________, you mean that they cause you to be alert and ready for anything that might happen.

Practice

A ***Select the correct idiom A, B or C to complete the following sentences.***

1 A common fear voiced by privatisation's critics is that companies will ______________ in order to make money off the contracts.

A pull their weight *B cut corners* *C be up to scratch*

2 Amid the turmoil, the belief by half those surveyed that men simply refuse to ______________________ around the home is one of the biggest grievances. Ironically, unmarried women who live with their partners get more help than those who are married.

A pull their weight *B keep them on their toes* *C cut corners*

3 'You never know what a volcano will do,' he says. 'They certainly ______________________.'

A are up to scratch *B pull their weight* *C keep you on your toes*

4 Any investigator ______________ knows that you don't catch fish without some bait.

A pulling their weight *B cutting corners* *C worth his salt*

5 'His ______________, both as a producer and as a commissioner is second to none. His brief will be to deliver the best commercial schedule of quality programmes to attract a large and varied audience.'

A track record *B cutting corners* *C up to scratch*

6 Guides are assessed every year, and although they're not paid, they don't necessarily have a job for life either – they can be dismissed if they're ______________________.

A keeping on their toes *B not up to scratch* *C pulling their weight*

B ***Complete the following sentences with one of the idioms in this unit, paying special attention to the verb forms.***

1 Labour's controversial party political broadcast was masterminded by a man with ____________________ of powerful film-making.

2 Radio is about communication, and we will rely on listeners to ____________________ ____________________ and ensure that communication is of the highest quality.

3 When services bought from the private sector are ____________________, the customer gets his money back.

4 'I suppose I have to learn to say no to all these pressures. You see, I'm angry with my mum. She expects me to do her shopping and give her a lot of my time, when I have a sister who does not ____________________ and has more free time than I do.'

5 No journalist ____________________ wastes so much of his spare time and energy in the pursuit of a story!

6 In the private sector, government encouragement of low-cost housing, despite high land prices, means that builders save money by ____________________.

Consolidation

Write a paragraph on one of the following topics, using at least three of the idioms you have studied in this unit.

1 The competition.

2 Promotion.

3 An adventure.

UNIT 7: HONESTY AND FAIRNESS

above board	**not pull your punches**
not mince your words	**stab someone in the back**
come clean	**a level playing field**

Study the following examples to try and understand the underlined idioms in context.

above board

'I have never taken a penny of any of the money we've raised for the ministry. And anyone who wants to inspect our books can see for themselves that we are totally above board.'

not mince your words

Curry did not mince his words[1]. 'I'm absolutely disgusted with the attitude of the players,' the Australian said.

come clean

The banks say that most mistakes have already been corrected but a consumer group claims the mix-up could cost millions of pounds. 'The banks have come clean this time but it is by no means an isolated incident,' said Jean Eaglesham of the Consumers' Association money group. 'What is worrying is that no one can ever know how many administration errors are on customer accounts.'

not pull your punches

Deterring Democracy, by Noam Chomsky, is a controversial analysis of post-war American imperialism in which Chomsky, as usual, does not pull his punches[1]. He has no time for the much-discussed 'new world order'.

stab someone in the back

'She seemed to be incredibly disloyal,' said the same woman. 'She would be your friend to your face, and then stab you in the back. When confronted, she would say you imagined it. She would play people off against each other by telling each that the other was vindictive and jealous.'

a level playing field

The Games have always been meant to find the fastest and strongest on a level playing field[2]. In the ancient Games the judges had canes to beat runners who tried to get an unfair advantage by starting early, while in the modern Games athletes are often suspected of using drugs to gain a more surreptitious advantage.

LANGUAGE COMMENT

[1] **Not mince your words** and **not pull your punches** mean almost the same.
[2] **A level playing field** is particularly common in written English.

Meaning

Using your understanding of the sentences above, complete the following sentences with the correct idioms.

1 You use ____________________ to refer to a situation that is fair. You usually use this expression when talking about the fact that a situation is not fair, or when saying that you think it should be fair.

2 If you do ______________________________, you say what you want to say clearly and directly, without avoiding its unpleasant aspects.

3 If you describe a situation or business as __________________, you mean that it is honest and legal.

4 If you do ___________________________________ when you are giving an opinion, you state it clearly and directly, even though you know that some people will not like what you are saying.

5 If you say that someone you trusted ______________________________, you mean that they have done something which hurts and betrays you.

6 If someone _________________________ about something, they tell the truth about it.

Practice

A ***Select the correct idiom, A, B or C to complete the following sentences.***

1 'I believe that he is perhaps one of the leading writers of the 20th century, because his novels are also extremely important. He has a unique voice, I think, and he says things in a way more directly than other writers sometimes do. He doesn't ______________.'

A stab people in the back *B come clean* *C mince his words*

2 'Obviously, in a movie you have to condense, so sometimes we take three or four characters and we make them into one. And I ________________ about that. I'm not trying to hide anything. But I do think that it is the artist's, filmmaker's right and duty to confront and interpret history as that artist sees fit.'

A haven't come clean *B have pulled my punches* *C have been very above board*

3 I'm really surrounded by a very hypocritical bunch of people, who want to kiss me every time they see me, and then they ________________________.

A mince their words *B stab me in the back* *C come clean*

4 The Post Office chairman Sir Brian Nicholson said he welcomed the extra competition, so long as it was ________________ that allowed the Post Office to compete effectively.

A a stab in the back *B a level playing field* *C above board*

5 Finance companies should __________________ about why customers are refused credit, the director general of Fair Trading said yesterday. Sir Gordon Borrie issued a report on credit scoring, a points system that helps decide on giving credit by giving people points for age, job and residential status. He urged lenders to give specific reasons for refusal.

A mince their words *B pull their punches* *C come clean*

6 In a brave and clever speech he struck the same tone. He didn't ____________, repeating his calls for a public sector pay freeze, but also attacking directors' pay rises.

A pull his punches *B have a level playing field* *C come clean*

B ***Complete the following sentences with one of the idioms in this unit, paying special attention to the verb forms.***

1 And if you are caught out in anything not strictly ________________, you may find yourself having to provide the taxman with old bank statements and proofs of income going back years.

2 She had had enough of deceit and lies, of always having to cover up for her brother. She decided to ________________________ and tell her family everything that had happened.

3 British Airways officials were aghast at the level of aid being poured into their competitors. 'We can't compete on ___________________ while this goes on,' one said.

4 Hospital staff, fed up with treating youngsters for crime-related injuries, will tour Merseyside schools. 'We will ____. We are targeting 11 to 18-year olds. they are most likely to get caught up in drugs, pinching cars and fights. Once they have seen what can happen maybe they will think twice before getting involved.'

5 'I have a little advice, too. Now at NBC, they're pretty nice guys. They're not going to ___________________________. They like to see your face when they do it.'

6 New York Times music critic Peter Watress does ___________________________________ when it comes to Buddy Guy: 'Buddy Guy is one of the most virtuoso blues guitarists that's ever lived.'

Consolidation

Write a paragraph on one of the following topics, using at least three of the idioms you have studied in this unit.

1 Betrayal.

2 A political speech.

3 Honesty is the best policy.

UNIT 8: DECEPTION, HIDING AND REVEALING

pay lip service to something	**blow the whistle on someone**
go through the motions	**a stiff upper lip**
sweep something under the carpet	**keep something under wraps**

Study the following examples to try and understand the underlined idioms in context.

pay lip service to something

Despite the real advances made in equality for women in the workplace, maternity leave can still be a fast track to redundancy, unless care is taken to find firms which do not just pay lip service to equal rights.

go through the motions

As the taxi edged closer to the head of the queue, it became obvious that the police were carrying out thorough searches, not just going through the motions.

sweep something under the carpet

Its officials, the various team officials and the riders all need to learn from their experiences in Germany and accept their responsibilities. We must not sweep the issues under the carpet[1] and put the events of this year's European Championships down to bad luck.

blow the whistle on someone

Doctors have been urged to blow the whistle on colleagues with drink or health problems. Medical chiefs fear patient care could suffer at the hands of a doctor who refuses to seek help.

a stiff upper lip

I shared my feelings with no one because I had always believed in keeping a stiff upper lip, crying in private, and putting on my best face for family and friends. How wrong I was.

keep something under wraps

The strong impression of the past few days has been of a government determined to keep the report under wraps[2] for fear of exposing its own culpability.

LANGUAGE COMMENT

[1] Other verbs, such as 'brush' and 'push' are sometimes used instead of 'sweep'. **Sweep something under the rug,** which is more common in American English than in British English, means the same as **sweep something under the carpet**.

[2] Other verbs can be used instead of 'keep', such as 'remain'. **Take the wraps off something** means almost the opposite of **keep something under wraps**.

Meaning

Using your understanding of the sentences above, complete the following definitions with the correct idioms.

1 If you say that someone ______________________ an idea, you are being critical of them because they appear to be in favour of it, but are not doing anything to support it.

2 If something is ______________________, it is kept secret and not revealed to anyone.

3 If you ______________________ someone who is doing something illegal, dishonest or immoral, you tell the authorities about them because you feel strongly that what they are doing is wrong and they should be stopped.

4 If someone is keeping ______________________, they hide their emotions and do not let other people see what they are feeling. You can also refer to the attitude or behaviour of people who do not like to show their emotions as the ______________________.

5 If you say that someone is ______________________, you mean that they are doing something that they have to do or are expected to do, but without any real effort or enthusiasm.

6 If you ______________________, you try to hide it and forget about it because you find it shameful or embarrassing.

Practice

A ***Select the correct idiom A, B or C to complete the following sentences.***

1 Neither staff nor pupils are afraid to admit that life is not simple. Far from encouraging ______________, pupils are taught that nobody can find his or her identity alone, that failure may be our greatest learning point.

A a stiff upper lip *B blowing the whistle* *C paying lip service*

2 In a BBC interview, Miss Bhutto said the issue was far too important to be ______________.

A swept under the carpet *B a stiff upper lip* *C blown the whistle*

3 The official report has ______________ for months by legal objections from British Airways.

A paid lip service *B been kept under wraps* *C gone through the motions*

4 She clearly found the child primarily a bother, an obstacle to the satisfaction of her own needs. She ______________________, doing a few of the right things like taking Rosemary for haircuts or buying her clothes; but the relationship between mother and daughter was basically empty, punctuated by frequent, angry outbursts on both sides.

A went through the motions *B swept it under the carpet* *C blew the whistle*

5 It is becoming harder for staff to ______________________ bad practice or management in hospitals.

A pay lip service to *B blow the whistle on* *C sweep it under the carpet*

6 How do the police think that we are going to trust them, when we know that they lie about the files they hold on us and ____________ our rights as citizens?

A sweep under the carpet *B blow the whistle* *C pay lip service to*

B ***Complete the following sentences with one of the idioms in this unit, paying special attention to the verb forms.***

1 Bethany and Patrick raced to the murder scene to find Peter Ellis in a state of complete shock. 'He was showing no emotion,' said Bethany. 'He was drained, he was like a zombie.' Later they were all at the police station together. Bethany said: 'He was just ____________ like he was on auto-pilot. When they asked him how to get in touch with Julie's family he gave the numbers quite matter-of-factly. He was clearly in total shock.'

2 'I listened with interest to your story on juvenile corrections and was shocked to learn that these institutions don't seriously attempt to rehabilitate our young people. These institutions have never done more than ____________ helping troubled youngsters.'

3 'When I was a child, science – usually embodied by nuclear energy – was the great white hope. It was overhyped, and any drawbacks were discreetly ____________ ____________. Naturally, the next generation, thoroughly disillusioned, turned against science and into romantic, New Age pursuits. Now we are again admitting that an 'educated' person must know something of science.'

4 'We do have a new series coming out next year, but we're ____________ ____________ at the moment so I can't really tell you anything else.'

5 'I know the British tend to feel that problems have to be met with ____________, ____________ but there's more truth in the saying that a trouble shared is a trouble halved.'

6 Part of the settlement also requires Rockwell to distribute a memo to employees that calls on them to ____________ anyone who asks them to incorrectly record hours worked on their time forms.

Consolidation

Write a paragraph on one of the following topics, using at least three of the idioms you have studied in this unit.

1 The birthday party.

2 Dishonesty.

3 The secret.

UNIT 9: ANGER, IRRITATION, FRUSTRATION AND FEAR

a pain in the neck	**bite the bullet**
get on someone's nerves	**red tape**
a chip on your shoulder	**get cold feet**
the last straw	

Study the following examples to try and understand the underlined idioms in context.

a pain in the neck

They think that every time they win a game, get to the front of the traffic queue, make someone else look small, or win an argument, they are making themselves look important. But always being the best is a pain in the neck to others. Ordinary people who make mistakes and joke about them are much more fun to be with.

get on someone's nerves

'I love the people I work with here, I really do. But working that close to people and no matter how much you like them, you get on each other's nerves. That's just the way life works.'

a chip on your shoulder

He had a tremendous aura and a great talent for surrounding himself with an audience. He was also very aggressive, with an enormous chip on his shoulder about his childhood. His mother and father had split up when he was four and he was brought up by his Aunt Mimi.

the last straw

'Rocked by riots, floods, earthquakes and recession, residents are flocking to therapists. Inquiries at the University of California Anxiety Disorders Unit have leapt 50 per cent in the last six months. 'The earthquake was the last straw[1],' said director Alexander Bystritsky. 'Insomnia, panic attacks and depression are rising and marital therapists are working overtime,' said psychologist Penny Fischoff.

bite the bullet

'But the president does still appear to have a chance of convincing many Americans to bite the bullet. Poll after poll shows that a majority will pay higher taxes if they get better schools, affordable health care, and a smaller deficit in return.'

red tape

A group of doctors from the French charity, Medecins Sans Frontieres, have set up a dispensary in the camps. But they say they could have been ready days earlier if it hadn't been for red tape and bureaucracy.

get cold feet

I feel your boyfriend got cold feet about being in a committed relationship. He may even have fallen out of love.

LANGUAGE COMMENT

[1] **The last straw** is an abbreviation of the proverb **It's the last straw that breaks the camel's back. The final straw** means the same as **the last straw**.

Meaning

Using your understanding of the sentences above, complete the following definitions with the correct idioms.

1 If you ________________, you accept a difficult or unpleasant situation.

2 People refer to official rules and procedures as ________________ when they seem unnecessary and cause delay.

3 If you say that someone ________________, you mean that they feel angry and resentful because they think that they have been treated unfairly, especially because of their race, sex or background.

4 If you think that someone or something is very annoying, you can say that they are a ________________.

5 If you say that something is ________________, you mean it is the latest in a series of unpleasant or difficult events, and it makes you feel that you cannot tolerate a situation any longer.

6 If you ________________ or have ________________ about something, you are not sure whether you want to do it, or you become too nervous and worried to do it.

7 If you say that someone or something ________________, you mean that they annoy or irritate you.

Practice

A ***Select the correct idiom A, B or C to complete the following sentences.***

1 Danielle said his job put her husband under enormous pressure and he had become unbearable to live with. 'The phone used to ________________, people ringing him at home as if it was an extension of the office,' she said. 'He was miserable and sullen all the time and rows would start over petty things.'

A get cold feet *B bite the bullet* *C get on my nerves*

2 The new Industry Commissioner in Brussels yesterday pledged to fight European Commission ________________, promising that all new legislation will be tested for its impact on small businesses.

A last straw *B red tape* *C cold feet*

3 The Spanish are also believed to be _______________ over their slice of the £60 billion cost.

A red tape *B getting cold feet* *C the last straw*

4 Lady Ottoline, though bitterly hurt, never fought back. She _______________ and carried on. While she may not have been a 'great' woman, she was certainly a brave one.

A got cold feet *B got on my nerves* *C bit the bullet*

5 To be informed in a recent article that divorced people are a huge financial burden on the rest of the population is really _________________. Since my husband left six years ago I have battled to give my kids a decent life.

A the last straw *B red tape* *C biting the bullet*

6 My father wasn't always easy to get along with; he had ___________________ and thought people didn't like him because of his colour.

A a pain in the neck *B a chip on his shoulder* *C the last straw*

7 Evan is 11 years old, bright and ____________________. He hits his classmates. He steals and smokes and puts paint in teacher's coffee. On a picnic, he sets fire to a tree.

A getting cold feet *B the last straw* *C a pain in the neck*

B ***Complete the following sentences with one of the idioms from this unit, paying special attention to the verb forms.***

1 If you're one of the 350,000 couples getting married this year there is insurance to cover disaster on the big day. It costs around £35, depending on the cover offered, and will pay out if either of you are forced to call off plans, though _______________ on the part of bride or groom is not covered.

2 'Those owners who are __________________________ and being totally realistic about asking prices are selling their houses. But there are still at least 30% of the people we advise who refuse to drop their prices. Invariably those properties will not sell.'

3 In the summer of 1941, only 10 per cent of the nation's productive capacity was being devoted to defense production; the preparedness program was plagued by apathy, bottlenecks, _______________, indecision, overlapping bureaucratic jurisdictions, and a shocking lack of coordination, all of which created what Senator Harry Byrd of Virginia termed a state of general confusion and dangerous delay.

4 Retired music consultant Frank Reidy, 70, said: 'I feel there are enough restaurants and cafes in this district. Within half a mile, I've counted 40 restaurants. I've nothing against McDonald's, but we don't need any more eateries. McDonald's opening will be ___________________ that breaks the camel's back.'

5 'It's all down to my new family responsibilities as a father,' Paul explained. 'Before he arrived, I used to be a _____________________________ when I got home from work. If we lost, I would be in a right mood and be difficult to live with for my wife Claire.'

6 'I don't want him to have __________________________________ for the rest of his life because of what's happened to his mother and what will soon happen to me. Everybody dies one day.'

7 'The plot was excellent and the soundtrack really haunting,' he said. Sheila McGachey, 18, was more critical, saying: 'Anne Archer, who plays the hero's wife, ____, although not enough to spoil it.' But there was more praise from Linda Tallon, 30, who said: 'I've seen every Harrison Ford film and I've never been disappointed.'

Consolidation

Write a paragraph on one of the following topics, using at least three of the idioms you have studied in this unit.

1 The most annoying person I know.

2 The airport.

3 A problem.

UNIT 10: DISAGREEMENT

not see eye to eye with someone	**at loggerheads**
a bone of contention	**at odds with someone/something**
go against the grain	

Study the following examples and try to understand the underlined idioms in context.

not see eye to eye with someone

'Then I saw Linford. We hadn't seen eye to eye for the past couple of months, and there was still a bit of friction between us. But he came over and put his arms out and we just embraced. It sounds soppy and stupid, but it's something money can't buy.'

a bone of contention

He thought that the only bone of contention between the pro- and anti-hunting campaigners was whether foxes should be killed by hounds. 'Everyone agrees that foxes have to be killed. The question is how.'

go against the grain

'I myself have an eighteen year-old daughter, and I tell you it goes against the grain to have to seriously consider girls of her age and younger as murder suspects. But we have no choice, do we?'

at loggerheads

It shows that, at a time of international crisis, the two superpowers, who in previous years would have been at loggerheads in such a situation, are working together and are determined to go on doing so. That is very promising indeed.

at odds with someone/something

It is still structured around an elite that bases its tastes and values on those of the West. Thus, the official language is English, although a small percentage speak it well. There is a spirit of consumerism that is at odds with the widespread poverty. Also, the long cultural traditions are considered inferior to Coca-Cola culture.

Meaning

Using your understanding of the sentences above, complete the following sentences with the correct idioms.

1 If you say that an idea or action ________________________, you mean that it is very difficult for you to accept or do, because it conflicts with your ideas, beliefs or principles.

2 If one person or group is ________________________ with another, they strongly disagree about something.

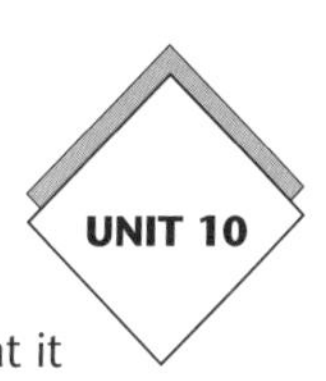

3 If you say that one thing is ______________________ another, you mean that it does not match or correspond to that other thing.

4 If you do not ______________________ someone, you do not agree with them about something.

5 A ______________________ is an issue or point that people have been arguing about for a long time.

Practice

A ***Select the correct idiom A, B or C to complete the following sentences.***

1 He is more closely involved in team selection than any chairman in Britain dares to be. When managers have ______________________ with him, the classic case being Franz Beckenbauer, who lasted less than a year, his autocratic style has seen them replaced.

A not been at loggerheads *B not seen eye to eye* *C not been at odds*

2 'It's hard to fight your bosses. It's hard to fight the boss if he's made his mind up or you're constantly ______________________ with him.'

A seeing eye to eye *B a bone of contention* *C at loggerheads*

3 Many groups of animals suddenly disappeared. Among them were the dinosaurs. What caused these mass extinctions has been ______________________ for geologists for years.

A a bone of contention *B at loggerheads* *C eye to eye*

4 As an entrepreneur, you're going to run into more than your fair share of pessimists. By his nature, the entrepreneur is often ______________________ popular opinion.

A a bone of contention with *B seeing eye to eye with* *C going against the grain of*

5 Mr Williams is ______________________ other city officials over how best to introduce reforms.

A at odds with *B going against the grain* *C a bone of contention with*

B ***Complete the following sentences with one of the idioms in this unit, paying special attention to the verb forms.***

1 If there was work anywhere, he would have to take it. It ______________________ of everything he believed in and hoped for. It was giving up or running away when he knew he was needed, but he would do it because it was for Dickon.

2 'They had just witnessed the most traumatic season in the history of West Bromwich Albion. Everyone seemed to be ______________________ with everyone: the management, the board, the players, the supporters and the media. The players were afraid to go out and play football. They knew that if they made a mistake the crowd would have a go at them.'

3 The father and son have a reputation for mutual competitiveness. Sir Kingsley, now 70, once remarked how his son, as a young man, would cover up anything he was writing when father walked into the room. But although they do ____________________ on politics – Sir Kingsley is proudly right-wing, while Martin, 42, is a staunch Labour supporter – both clearly have the same masterly touch with the written word.

4 Why did the authorities take so long to confirm the scale of the tragedy? Could they have done more to prevent it? And what reassurances can they give about the future? Some people have returned home with accounts of what happened which are ____________________ the official version.

5 Invited to adjudicate a dispute over barking dogs, a court in the western German town of Hamm has attempted a final solution to an age-old ____________________. It concluded that the neighbours would have to put up with a certain amount of barking from the animals. But dogs should not be allowed to bark for longer than 30 minutes a day, nor for more than 10 minutes at a time. They should bark only between 8am and 1pm, and between 3pm and 7pm. The ruling is now being explained to the dogs.

Consolidation

Write a paragraph on one of the following topics, using at least three of the idioms you have studied in this unit.

1 An argument.

2 The next-door neighbour.

3 Politics.

the writing is on the wall	**on the right track**
back to the drawing board	**in the doldrums**
throw in the towel	**out of the blue**
plain sailing	**on the cards**
make headway	**in the pipeline**
the light at the end of the tunnel	

Study the following examples to try and understand the underlined idioms in context.

the writing is on the wall

Last month, BNC's 40 employees were called into the works canteen and told their services were no longer required. Only a skeleton staff remains to show anyone interested around the site. For the staff, the writing is on the wall[1]. They know it is unlikely that they will work there again.

back to the drawing board

Not all high-tech projects did well in the Clinton administration's economic plan: NASA was sent back to the drawing board[2] to come up with a streamlined proposal for its space station.

throw in the towel

'It took me quite a few months to get motivated again, and even at that point I was so fed up of waiting I was ready to throw in the towel[3]. But my family told me not to give up. They convinced me it would work out and it did.'

plain sailing

'There we all work for the common good,' he said. But that does not mean that everything is plain sailing. One of his current struggles involves a conflict between saving the environment, which he supports, and small businesses, which he also supports.

make headway

'Still, if the patient has a problem with which I am not making headway, then it might be very cost-effective for me to bring in someone who is a specialist in that area.'

the light at the end of the tunnel

'I've been going out to work every day as a labourer. It motivates you, getting out to work, and you can see the light at the end of the tunnel.'

on the right track

'And when it comes to meal times, the Italian love of pasta also puts them on the right track[4]. Carbohydrates in large quantities, such as pasta, are the perfect foodstuff for anyone who has to do a lot of exercise every day,' says sports dietician Jill Horgan from the National Institute of Sports Medicine.

in the doldrums

With the housing market <u>*in the doldrums*</u>*, lenders are making desperate efforts to attract new custom. But as soon as it picks up, these offers will vanish like snow. So take advantage while you can.*

out of the blue

'Don't always do what is expected; I have often taken a reduction in salary and position to move in a new direction.' One such change came when he sent a letter <u>*out of the blue*</u> *to David Sainsbury requesting a job. He was then 34 years old. A year later, he was on the board.*

on the cards

'I don't know if marriage is <u>*on the cards*</u>[5] *– it's too early to say.'*

in the pipeline

'It's been 21 years <u>*in the pipeline*</u>[6]*, but next April the US rail company Amtrak will launch a coast-to-coast service from Los Angeles to Miami. Amtrak will use its new double-decked Superliners and, with a 58-hour journey schedule, there should be plenty of time to admire the view.'*

LANGUAGE COMMENT

[1] In American English, **the handwriting is on the wall** means the same as **the writing is on the wall**.

[2] **Back to square one** means almost the same as **back to the drawing board**. If you refer to something as being **on the drawing board**, it means it is not finished yet.

[3] Verbs such as 'chuck' and 'toss' are sometimes used instead of 'throw'. **Throw in the sponge** is the same as **throw in the towel**, but less common.

[4] **On the wrong track** means the opposite of **on the right track**.

[5] In American English, **in the cards** means the same as **on the cards**.

[6] In American English, **in the works** means the same as **in the pipeline**.

Meaning

Using your understanding of the sentences above, complete the following sentences with the correct idioms.

1 If something happens ____________________, it happens unexpectedly.

2 If an economy or business is __________________________, nothing new is happening and it is not doing very well.

3 If you say that __________________________________, you mean that you have noticed things which suggest strongly that a situation is going to become difficult or unpleasant.

4 If you say that you will have to go ____, you mean that something which you have done has not been successful and you will have to start again or try another idea.

5 If you say that something is ____________________, you mean that it is very likely to happen.

6 If something is ________________, it is being planned or is in progress.

7 If you say that an activity or task will not be ________________, you mean that it will be difficult to do or achieve. If it will be easy to achieve or do, you can say that it is ________________.

8 If you are ________________, you are acting or progressing in a way that is likely to result in success.

9 If you ________________, you make progress in the thing you are trying to achieve.

10 If you refer to ________________, you are referring to something which gives you hope about the future and for the end of a difficult or unpleasant situation.

11 If someone ________________, they stop trying to do something, because they know they cannot succeed.

Practice

A ***Select the correct idiom A, B or C to complete the following sentences.***

1 ________________ for Capriati when she lost the first set 6-1 in less than 20 minutes, failing to win a single one of her service games and serving four double faults.

A Throw in the towel | *B Plain sailing* | *C The writing was on the wall*

2 'He had a heart bypass at 63! Can you imagine? If I were in his position at that age, I'd just ________________. Why go through all that just to try to live a normal life at that age?'

A go back to the drawing board | *B make headway* | *C throw in the towel*

3 'Sterling was particularly affected by all the devaluation talk over the weekend and by the feeling that the economy is ________________.'

A on the right track | *B in the doldrums* | *C making headway*

4 With only 18 days before the start of the Grand Prix season, the McLaren team has been forced ________________ after complaints from its two leading drivers that they cannot fit comfortably into the cockpits of their new cars – estimated to be worth £50 million – and, consequently, are driving slower than their rivals.

A back to the drawing board | *B to make headway* | *C in the pipeline*

5 Before committing to long courses, make sure you're taking the best one. Find someone in the field you want to work in who can make sure you are ________________.

A in the pipeline | *B out of the blue* | *C on the right track*

6 The idea is to make it easier for farmers to spray against weeds without killing the crop, thus increasing yield. Other changes ________________ may make plants more resistant to pests or diseases, able to survive drought or frost, or to produce sweeter, more nutritious or longer-lasting crops.

A *on the right track* *B* *in the pipeline* *C* *in the doldrums*

7 As Phillippa found, even with the ideal tenant, it isn't all ________________. 'If you are used to having your own home to yourself, it's difficult at first to get used to sharing the kitchen and the bathroom and so on,' she admits.

A *plain sailing* *B* *in the pipeline* *C* *the light at the end of the tunnel*

8 I have recently had a letter to say that, ________________, she received a fairly substantial sum of money, a legacy from an aunt, which will enable her to stay in her apartment, hopefully for the rest of her life.

A *out of the blue* *B* *in the pipeline* *C* *on the cards*

9 Marketing and sales bring high rewards. Given the right company, an annual salary of £70,000 to £90,000 may well be ________________.

A *making headway* *B* *on the right track* *C* *on the cards*

10 This season has been a big disappointment for everyone connected with the club, especially after we thought we were ________________ last season.

A *in the pipeline* *B* *in the doldrums* *C* *making headway*

11 As the first, most traumatic phase of motherhood draws to a conclusion towards the end of the second month, you will begin to see ________________ and begin to feel strong enough to go back to work.

A *plain sailing* *B* *out of the blue* *C* *the light at the end of the tunnel*

B ***Complete the following sentences with one of the idioms in this unit, paying special attention to the verb forms.***

1 'I did everything I could think of to get work,' he said. 'I'm a workaholic and I made a job out of finding a job. I know how easy it is to feel low but you can't let it get the better of you. At times I thought there really was no ________________ and the way things were going it did not look as though my chances were going to get any better.'

2 'For far too long, many museums have been kept ________________ by those responsible for running them. Early retirement has been used to solve such problems but is no substitute for proper training and increased opportunities for career progress.'

3 The Green Party failed to ________________ any ________________. They took just 1.3% of the vote.

4 None of us likes rejection, although it may be less wounding if the news comes as no surprise, or if your partner has been thinking along similar lines. If you suddenly announce ________________ that you want a divorce to a partner who is unaware of any problems, the shock will be incalculable.

5 Arnold Schwartzenegger has terminated rumours that he has plans to enter politics. He said: 'I have no interest in running for office. My interest is totally in show business and doing charitable activities. With all the movies I have ______________________, I don't have the time.'

6 A solicitor can set you ______________________ with independent advice on finding a suitable mortgage and placing your property on the market.

7 'I'm ready to ______________________, about to give up. Instead of doing their job, the directors are making statements on television and to the newspapers,' the Anatolian news agency quoted Toshack as saying.

8 Glore has been at her Red Hill recycling shop for years. But it is not all ______________ ______________for such shops, with four in the Paddington area shutting down in the last year.

9 She is reluctant to talk about potential new lines, but said the firm might move away from its traditional concentration on canned products. 'Development of fresh food ranges appears to be ______________________. Packing technology is improving all the time.'

10 In some families that I have seen break up, ______________________ from the beginning. The partners may have known, on some level, that the relationship wasn't working, even before the child came into the picture.

11 As technology has matured, earlier generations of systems and products have become obsolete. Banks are going ______________________ to do what consultants call process-engineering – re-designing the way they create and deliver products to their customers.

Consolidation

Write a paragraph on one of the following topics, using at least five of the idioms you have studied in this unit.

1 The football team.

2 Recession.

3 A plan.

UNIT 12: TROUBLE AND DIFFICULTY, SAFETY AND RISK

out on a limb	**a vicious circle**
put something on the line	**rock the boat**
have your back to the wall	**make waves**

Study the following examples to try and understand the underlined idioms in context.

out on a limb

If we apply the card to your career, it shows me that you fear change and would prefer to stay in your present situation even though it seems to be tiresome, rather than go out on a limb and try something new.

put something on the line

Sometimes the information is certified by a firm of accountants or investment bankers, who put their reputation on the line[1] when they endorse a company's report.

have your back to the wall

Everyone has written us off, but we have proved time and again we are never more dangerous than when we have our backs to the wall[2].

a vicious circle

And house prices are not rising. They are dropping. We are in the middle of a vicious circle. The more houses that are repossessed, the more will be up for sale, and the more prices will drop. And so it goes on.

rock the boat

But councils, thankfully, are made up of a wide variety of people. And, inevitably, there are a few who are seen as mavericks. Such people may cause the secretariat all sorts of problems as they unmercifully rock the boat. But they are also the people who frequently produce the useful reforms.

make waves

They are part of the new breed of furniture makers who are starting to make waves on the British scene.

LANGUAGE COMMENT

[1] **Put something on the line** is particularly common in written English.

[2] If someone or something **drives** or **pushes you to the wall**, they force you into a very difficult situation.

Meaning

Using your understanding of the sentences above, complete the following definitions with the correct idioms.

1 If you say that someone is ____________________, you mean that they are disturbing a situation by changing things or by challenging the way things are done. You sometimes use this expression to suggest that this is making things better or more exciting.

2 If you describe a difficult situation as ____________________, you are talking about how one problem has caused other problems which, in turn, have made the original problem even worse.

3 If someone is ____________________, their behaviour is likely to cause trouble or upset a stable situation.

4 If you go ____________________, you do something risky or extreme, which puts you in a position of weakness.

5 If you say that someone ______________________________, you mean that they have a very serious problem or are in a very difficult situation which will be hard to deal with.

6 If you __________ yourself, or something such as your job or your reputation ____________________, you do something which causes you to risk losing it.

Practice

A ***Select the correct idiom A, B or C to complete the following sentences.***

1 'Malcolm, I really had to ____________________ to get you that sort of deal. No-one else gets that sort of percentage.'

A *have my back to the wall* B *go out on a limb* C *be a vicious circle*

2 It is not a company with ____________________; they have just won a 13 billion-pound contract with Nuclear Electric.

A *its back to the wall* B *a vicious circle* C *a rocking boat*

3 He was still stunned that Hank had put his restaurant ________________. Hank's entire life was invested in the Crow's Nest.

A *in a vicious circle* B *out on a limb* C *on the line*

4 She believed that as the first woman to become an assistant chief constable she had a responsibility for championing her own cause. An early sign that Miss Halford was about to ____________________ came in an article she wrote for Police Review, which gave a pessimistic appraisal of women's chances of reaching the top. There was strong but covert resentment of women, she said.

A *rock the boat* B *have her back to the wall* C *be a vicious circle*

5 Ten years after his death, the best-known surrealist artist continues to __________.

A *make waves* B *have his back to the wall* C *put it on the line*

6 'If I was miserable I looked for the comfort of food, but it made me fat and unhappy and the ________________ would start again.'

A *rocking the boat* B *making waves* C *vicious circle*

B ***Complete the following sentences with one of the idioms in this unit, paying special attention to the verb forms.***

1 You're doing the right thing. If we don't ____________________ about it, we'll never get the local councillors or the local MP to even look at it.

2 I do ____________________________. I had no witnesses, and he's got his staff who'll back him to the hilt.

3 When the Radical Party's Raul Alfonsin came to power, he bought social peace by not ________________________________ economically.

4 He said his organisation was concerned about the increasing number of police officers who were armed while on duty. 'Of course police want to protect themselves, but the reality is that this is ________________________. Criminals who expect to encounter armed police are more likely themselves to carry arms.'

5 In its editorial, the Sunday Express says the young men of the Seventh Brigade know that if war comes, their lives will be _____________________________________, as there will be no easy or painless victory.

6 They've never learned how to go ____________________. They're afraid to make mistakes.

Consolidation

Write a paragraph on one of the following topics, using at least three of the idioms you have studied in this unit.

1 A dangerous situation.

2 Making changes.

3 A problem.

UNIT 13: MONEY

feel the pinch	**down the drain**
tighten your belt	**on a shoestring**
make ends meet	**in the red**

Study the following examples to try and understand the underlined idioms in context.

feel the pinch

Students bring substantial economic benefits to college towns. The smaller university centres in Wales like Aberystwyth, Bangor or Lampeter would really feel the pinch if there were fewer students.

tighten your belt

Having taken the trouble to draw up your budget, try very hard to stick to it. Clearly, if you are spending more than your income, you'll need to tighten your belt.

make ends meet

Nicola Gibbon went back to work as a night-shift nurse in Bristol after the birth of her fourth child. She said: 'I had to. Although my husband works, it's a juggling act making ends meet with four children, a mortgage and other considerations.'

down the drain

The survey reveals that some of the £55 million spent on new mouthwashes and rinses in Britain last year could be money down the drain. It says that brushing teeth is crucial and flossing is good. But it asks whether mouthwashes, chewing gums and special brushes live up to their claims.

on a shoestring

Things at TV-AM are now being run on a shoestring and it comes as quite a surprise that the staff are still permitted by management to waste electricity on running the cameras.

in the red

'When you read about massive layoffs, when you read about companies that are operating in the red[1], that are going through bankruptcies, those are clear signals that these are hard times.

LANGUAGE COMMENT

[1] **In the black** is the opposite of **in the red**.

Meaning

Using your understanding of the sentences above, complete the following definitions with the correct idioms.

1 If you say that something is going ____________________ you mean that it is getting worse or being destroyed and that it is unlikely to recover.

2 If you do something ____________________, you do it using very little money.

3 If you find it difficult to ____________________, you find it difficult to pay for the things you need in life, because you have very little money.

4 If a person or organization is ____________________, they owe money to someone, or to another organization.

5 If you have to ____________________, you must spend less and live more carefully because you have less money than you used to have.

6 If a person or company is ____________________, they do not have as much money as they used to have, and so they cannot buy the things they would like to buy.

Practice

A ***Select the correct idiom A, B or C to complete the following sentences.***

1 Steve Davis is 27 years old. He says he has trouble ____________________ because he can't find work and he's been unemployed for three months.

A on a shoestring *B feeling the pinch* *C making ends meet*

2 Kemp said Americans and industry shouldn't be asked to pay new taxes. Instead, he said, government should ____________________.

A tighten its belt *B feel the pinch* *C go down the drain*

3 'There is no more urgent problem in Britain today than the small businesses which are going ____________________ because of the failed economic policies of this Government.'

A down the drain *B to make ends meet* *C on a shoestring*

4 There may be room for reform at the UN, but that doesn't justify countries not paying their dues. I don't know of one single institution of excellence, whether academic, corporate, governmental, that is run ____________________ basis or hand to mouth.

A on a shoestring *B down the drain* *C in the red*

5 A Creditline overdraft allows you to continue obtaining cash and writing cheques even when your account is ____________________.

A making ends meet *B down the drain* *C in the red*

6 If growth in the US starts to crumble – as is looking increasingly likely – then the whole world will start to ____________________.

A feel the pinch *B make ends meet* *C be in the red*

B ***Complete the following sentences with one of the idioms in this unit, paying special attention to the verb forms.***

1 'It's enough to live on but not enough to save much. Now there's been no work for three weeks, and housewives are ______________________. Fatemah says she worries about money a lot, although there's no real hunger yet. Her family has changed its eating habits, no more meat or chicken and more of whatever is cheap and available – rice, eggplants, bananas.'

2 It is immediately apparent that a student has more chance of ______________________ financially if no return daily journeys are necessary between accommodation and college.

3 Harvey Nichols, one of London's poshest stores, is still deep ________________. The Knightsbridge operation has doubled its losses to £3.5m over the last 12 months.

4 Declining advertising revenue, coupled with falling circulation, means that papers are run ______________________. Consequently, they employ very few staff and use antiquated equipment – the newspapers are of low quality, poorly designed and devoid of any colour.

5 It is possible that Britain could have defended her commitments more adequately if she had been willing to ______________________________________ to pay for them.

6 'I just decided I was throwing money ________________________ renting, and I'd always wanted my own place. I'd recommend anybody in my situation to do the same as me.'

Consolidation

Write a paragraph on one of the following topics, using at least three of the idioms you have studied in this unit.

1 The lottery.

2 The refugee.

3 Student life.

toe the line	**get out of hand**
pass the buck	**the upper hand**
pecking order	**call the shots**
wash your hands of something	**over the top**
pull strings	**draw the line**

Study the following examples to try and understand the underlined idioms in context.

toe the line

Practices such as threats to withhold supply from dealers who fail to toe the line[1] on prices have helped to sustain Britain's dubious record as one of the most expensive countries in the world in which to buy a new car.

pass the buck

The government says it's up to the Medical Board. Health Rights don't want to know. I contacted a federal MP and he says it's not a Federal Government problem. Everybody seems to be passing the buck[2] all the time.

the pecking order

'Egalitarianism had always been my thing as a student,' says Anne, who now works in insurance. 'But I soon realised that office hierarchies are very clearly defined, and someone has to make the tea. Challenging the strict pecking order was certainly not the way to further my career.'

wash your hands of something

The European Union has been considering adopting a common immigration policy. The report accuses European governments of washing their hands of responsibility for political refugees, treating them as illegal immigrants, not people fleeing persecution.

pull strings

Marvin became one of many old friends to whom the Roosevelts remained loyal, despite his weaknesses. His drinking drove him from job to job for years; loans from Eleanor and Franklin kept him alive and they pulled strings several times to find him positions they thought he might be able to fill.

get out of hand

Judge Grant Britten said the incident had started off as a school yard fight and then changed once the defendant picked up the knife, resulting in the fight getting out of hand.

the upper hand

The director of the Kenya Wildlife Service, Dr Richard Leakey, has said he's hoping to gain the upper hand in the fight against ivory poachers by supplying his patrols with new surveillance equipment. Dr Leakey is in Britain for the start of an experiment in which the movements of several Kenyan elephants will be monitored by satellite.

call the shots

The real issue is that Ferguson, at that time, was truly in charge. He had absolute control. He called the shots[3].

over the top

'I remember her walking in on the first day in a yellow polo-neck, green stripy tights and a pink skirt. She looked incredible. Her hats are over the top[4] *and eccentric, just like her, really.'*

draw the line

This said, adults have the right to make decisions for themselves about what makes them feel and look better. Where does one draw the line and say that one form of cosmetic change is acceptable and another is not? It is a complicated area where our feelings about ourselves interface with the ever-changing social ideas about beauty.

LANGUAGE COMMENT

[1] **Toe the line** is very often used in domestic politics in this way: **toe the party line**.

[2] To say **the buck stops here** means the opposite of **pass the buck**.

[3] **Call the tune** means almost the same as **call the shots**. **Call the tune** comes from the saying **he who pays the piper calls the tune**.

[4] **Over the top** can be abbreviated to **OTT** in British English.

Meaning

Using your understanding of the sentences above, complete the following definitions with the correct idioms.

1 If you describe something as ____________________, you are being critical of it because you think it is extreme and exaggerated.

2 If you accuse someone of ____________________, you are accusing them of failing to take responsibility for a problem, and of expecting someone else to deal with it instead.

3 The ____________________ in a group is the order of importance of the people or things within that group.

4 If someone ____________________ to get something they want, they get it by using their friendships with powerful and influential people, often in a way that is considered unfair.

5 If you refuse to ____________________, you refuse to behave in the way that people in authority expect you to behave. If you ____________________, you behave in the way they expect.

6 If you talk about knowing where to ____________________, you are talking about knowing at what point an activity or situation stops being reasonable and starts being unacceptable.

7 If someone ____________________, they control everything that another person or an organization does.

8 If you ____________________ a problem or of a person who causes problems, you refuse to be involved with them or to take responsibility for them any longer.

9 If a situation or a person ____________________, they cannot be controlled any longer.

10 If one side has ____________________ in a competitive situation, it has more power than the other side and can control things. If one side gains ____________________, it gets more power and becomes able to control things.

Practice

A ***Select the correct idiom A, B or C to complete the following sentences.***

1 American TV pays the money, so they ____________________. There is no boxing without America.

A *pull strings* B *get out of hand* C *call the shots*

2 The first focus was on discipline. Once I'd convinced the children that I wasn't going to desert them, I told them, 'There are certain things I won't tolerate. Either you ____________________, or you leave.'

A *call the shots* B *toe the line* C *pass the buck*

3 No one gets fired these days, and no one gets laid off. If you're high enough in the corporate ____________________, you resign for personal reasons, an orderly transition between career changes.

A *passing the buck* B *pecking order* C *upper hand*

4 Yesterday's bombing will be seen as a further indication that the violent element of the animal rights lobby is gaining ____________________.

A *the pecking order* B *the buck* C *the upper hand*

5 'My kids are great,' he says. 'Sure, they were overprivileged, but I never allowed it to ____________________.'

A *pull strings* B *get out of hand* C *call the shots*

6 'The controversy over sexual harassment has left a lot of people confused. Men complain they don't know what they can and cannot say anymore. Women wonder exactly where they should ____________________.'

A *draw the line* B *get out of hand* C *pass the buck*

7 Everyone was expensively dressed, although some of the women were decidedly ____________________.

A *pulling the strings* B *drawing the line* C *over the top*

8 His powerful father-in-law Thomas, at that point personnel director of the Finance Ministry, ________________, and Tiburce was offered the job of subprefect at Yssingeaux on February 20, 1836.

A *got out of hand* *B* *pulled strings* *C* *toed the line*

9 Tour operators like to ____________. Their brochures normally exclude liability for lost or damaged luggage and say you must claim on the airline or on your own insurance.

A *pass the buck* *B* *toe the line* *C* *get out of hand*

10 She was never going to change. He'd __________________ her. What she did with her life was her own affair.

A *drawn the line* *B* *passed the buck to* *C* *washed his hands of*

B ***Complete the following sentences with one of the idioms in this unit, paying special attention to the verb forms.***

1 'Ken Livingstone is a very entertaining talker. He's one of the politicians that wouldn't ________________party ______________. He speaks his mind.'

2 'We cannot ______________________________ responsibility for the state of the economy. If Prime Ministers , Chancellors of the Exchequer and Secretaries of State have no control over the economy at all, then we might as well just all pack our bags and leave everything to unrestricted market forces.'

3 There is usually a ____________________, even with cats which are related and apparently compatible. The dominance can be expressed in different ways, sometimes by the chief cat washing the other one and sometimes by the occasional display of aggression.

4 In my experience of university life, it is the middle-class youth who often have less to offer. Many have little reason to care about their studies, having parents who can ____________ __________________ for them after they graduate. Working-class students, on the other hand, must have a great deal of motivation just to attempt a degree.

5 'Unfortunately, there were only two small exits from the site, and with a couple of hundred vehicles trying to get out, it soon ______________________________. They were ramming each other and driving through hedges to get out.'

6 This is a breathtaking remake of a 1960 shocker, and in a nice touch, the original Cady and Bowden, Robert Mitchum and Gregory Peck, show up in cameos. De Niro's portrayal, albeit __________________ at times, is magnificently chilling and Nolte too is superb as a once self-contained man whose life is blasted apart. Don't watch this alone.

7 Nowadays, I eat most things that are hot and dead. Although I ____________________ at eating something that's staring at me. I was in Indonesia recently making a film for the BBC when I was served a deep fried chicken with its head and feet left on. I just couldn't face it.

8 The Scottish oyster, overfished to the brink of extinction, is fighting back against the fat, Pacific cousin which ousted him 20 years ago. As the new oyster season starts this week, scientists and fish farmers predict the naturally grown native mollusc will gain ____________________________________ because it can breed more easily. Sex, for the Pacific oyster, is sadly a problem in Scotland's cold waters.

9 Film directors, in my experience, are the most awkward of the famous to interview because they are so used to controlling and ______________________.

10 'You're ______________________, professor! Don't try and shift the blame onto me, it had nothing to do with me, it was up to you to check.'

Consolidation

Write a paragraph on one of the following topics, using at least four of the idioms you have studied in this unit.

1 The manager.

2 The election campaign.

3 An accident.

Introductory unit

A Meanings and idioms

1C 2D 3E 4A 5B

B Grammar and idioms

verb + noun: rock the boat, break the ice
adjective + noun: the pecking order, a vicious circle
prepositional idiom: in the doldrums, from scratch
combination of types: turn a blind eye to something, turn over a new leaf

C Variations in idioms

1A,G 2A 3E 4A,F 5A,C
6A,C,G

D Restrictions

1
1 negative 2 positive
3 negative 4 negative
5 positive

2
1 plural 2 singular
3 singular 4 plural
5 singular 6 plural

3
1 passive 2 passive
3 active 4 active
5 passive

Unit 1 – Information and understanding, memory and mind

Meaning

1 get the hang of
2 hear something on the grapevine
3 out of your depth
4 crosses your mind
5 read between the lines
6 put your finger on something
7 rule of thumb
8 off the record
9 bear something in mind

Practice A

1B 2A 3C 4B 5C
6A 7C 8C 9C

Practice B

1 reading between the lines
2 heard on the grapevine
3 getting the hang of
4 put your finger
5 rule of thumb
6 out of your depth
7 off the record
8 bear in mind
9 crossed his mind

Unit 2 – Importance and priorities, decisions

Meaning

1 the icing on the cake
2 sitting on the fence
3 stick to your guns
4 the bottom line
5 the tip of the iceberg
6 up in the air
7 on the back burner

Practice A

1A 2C 3A 4C 5B
6B 7C

Practice B

1 up in the air
2 sit on the fence
3 the tip of the iceberg
4 the bottom line
5 sticking to your guns
6 the icing on the cake
7 put them on the back burner

Unit 3 – Communication, help and encouragement

Meaning

1 a silver lining
2 a pat on the back
3 hit it off
4 on the same wavelength
5 in the same boat
6 break the ice

Practice A

1A 2A 3C 4B 5A
6C

Practice B

1 in the same boat
2 a silver lining
3 a pat on the back
4 on the same wavelength
5 hit it off
6 break the ice

Unit 4 – Involvement and interest

Meaning

1 keep something at bay... keep people at bay
2 give you the cold shoulder
3 jumping on the bandwagon
4 has an axe to grind
5 at arm's length
6 turn a blind eye to
7 steer clear... steer someone clear
8 keeps a low profile

Practice A

1B 2B 3C 4C 5C
6B 7C 8C

Practice B

1 give him the cold shoulder
2 keep...at bay
3 steer clear
4 keep a low profile
5 at arm's length
6 have no axe to grind/don't have an axe to grind
7 jumping on the bandwagon
8 turning a blind eye

Unit 5 – Starting and stopping

Meaning

1 turned over a new leaf
2 nip...in the bud
3 from scratch
4 set the ball rolling
5 call it a day

Practice A

1C 2B 3B 4A 5C

Practice B

1 call it a day
2 from scratch
3 turned over a new leaf
4 set the ball rolling
5 nipped in the bud

Unit 6 – Quality and effort

Meaning

1 worth their salt
2 pulls their weight
3 not up to scratch
4 track record
5 cut corners
6 keeps you on your toes

Practice A

1B 2A 3C 4C 5A
6B

Practice B

1 a track record
2 keep us on our toes
3 not up to scratch
4 pull her weight
5 worth their/his/her salt
6 cutting corners

Unit 7 – Honesty and fairness

Meaning

1 a level playing field
2 not mince your words/not pull your punches
3 above board
4 not pull your punches/not mince your words
5 has stabbed you in the back
6 comes clean

Practice A

1C 2C 3B 4B 5C
6A

Practice B

1	above board
2	come clean
3	a level playing field
4	not be pulling our punches/not be mincing our words
5	stab you in the back
6	not mince his words/not pull his punches

Unit 8 – Deception, hiding and revealing

Meaning

1	pays lip service to
2	kept under wraps
3	blow the whistle on
4	a stiff upper lip... stiff upper lip
5	going through the motions
6	sweep something under the carpet

Practice A

1A 2A 3B 4A 5B
6C

Practice B

1	going through the motions
2	pay lip service to
3	swept under the carpet
4	keeping it under wraps
5	a stiff upper lip
6	blow the whistle on

Unit 9 – Anger, irritation, frustration and fear

Meaning

1	bite the bullet
2	red tape
3	has a chip on their shoulder
4	pain in the neck
5	the last straw
6	get ...cold feet
7	gets on your nerves

Practice A

1C 2B 3B 4C 5A
6B 7C

Practice B

1	cold feet
2	biting the bullet
3	red tape
4	the last straw
5	pain in the neck
6	a chip on his shoulder
7	got on my nerves

Unit 10 – Disagreement

Meaning

1	goes against the grain
2	at loggerheads
3	at odds with
4	see eye to eye with
5	bone of contention

Practice A

1B 2C 3A 4C 5A

Practice B

1	went against the grain
2	at loggerheads
3	not see eye to eye (with each other)
4	at odds with
5	bone of contention

Unit 11 – Success and failure, progress and expectation

Meaning

1	out of the blue
2	in the doldrums
3	the writing is on the wall
4	back to the drawing board
5	on the cards
6	in the pipeline
7	plain sailing... plain sailing
8	on the right track
9	make headway
10	the light at the end of the tunnel
11	throws in the towel

Practice A

1C 2C 3B 4A 5C
6B 7A 8A 9C 10C
11C

Practice B

1 light at the end of the tunnel
2 in the doldrums
3 make … headway
4 out of the blue
5 in the pipeline
6 on the right track
7 throw in the towel
8 plain sailing
9 on the cards
10 the writing is/was/has been on the wall
11 back to the drawing board

Unit 12 – Trouble and difficulty, safety and risk

Meaning

1 making waves
2 a vicious circle
3 rocking the boat
4 out on a limb
5 has their back to the wall
6 put... on the line

Practice A

1B 2A 3C 4A 5A
6C

Practice B

1 make waves
2 have my back to the wall
3 rocking the boat
4 a vicious circle
5 (put) on the line
6 out on a limb

Unit 13 – Money

Meaning

1 down the drain
2 on a shoestring
3 make ends meet
4 in the red
5 tighten your belt
6 feeling the pinch

Practice A

1C 2A 3A 4A 5C
6A

Practice B

1 feeling the pinch
2 making ends meet
3 in the red
4 on a shoestring
5 tighten her belt
6 down the drain

Unit 14 – Authority, responsibility, control and restriction

Meaning

1 over the top
2 passing the buck
3 pecking order
4 pulls strings
5 toe the line … toe the line
6 draw the line
7 calls the shots
8 wash your hands
9 gets out of hand
10 the upper hand … the upper hand

Practice A

1C 2B 3B 4C 5B
6A 7C 8B 9A 10C

Practice B

1 toe the … line
2 wash our hands of
3 pecking order
4 pull strings
5 got out of hand
6 over the top
7 draw the line
8 the upper hand
9 calling the shots
10 passing the buck

Collins
COBUILD

Idioms Workbook

The Collins COBUILD Idioms Workbook has been designed for use with the Collins COBUILD Dictionary of Idioms, but can also be used independently, either in class or for self-study. It provides helpful practice exercises which promote understanding and more natural use of the most common idioms in English.

- ✔ Fully updated and revised
- ✔ Detailed coverage of over 100 of the most common idioms
- ✔ Hundreds of real examples from the *Bank of English*
- ✔ Carefully graded activities to develop understanding
- ✔ Logical organization by theme
- ✔ Full answer key provided

Helping learners with real English

BANK OF ENGLISH

The *Bank of English* is a vast database of contemporary language from every imaginable source and style, totalling over *450 million words*. This unique resource is constantly updated to ensure that Collins dictionaries reflect the language of today.

To find out more about the *Bank of English*, about *Collins Wordbanks*, and about our online corpora,visit www.collinswordbanks.com

ISBN 0-00-713400-2
9 780007 134007 >